Made in the USA
Coppell, TX
24 June 2022

79219602R00057